Hundred Reason

Ideas Above our statio

Guitar Tablature Vocal

C000192600

Published 2002
© International Music Publications Limited
Griffin House, 161 Hammersmith Road, London, W6 8BS, England

Edited by Chris Harvey
Music arranged by Artemis Music Ltd
Photography by Steve Gullik / Dave Goodchild
Design & Illustration by Precession Industries (www.precession.org.uk)

I'll Find You

Words and Music by Andy Bews, Colin Doran, Andy Gilmour, Larry Hibbitt and Paul Townsend

Fig. 1

5

6

Taking the tra - il that leads will find you, find you.

*combined part - Gtr. 1 plays 3rd+5th strings, Gtr 2. plays 6th string

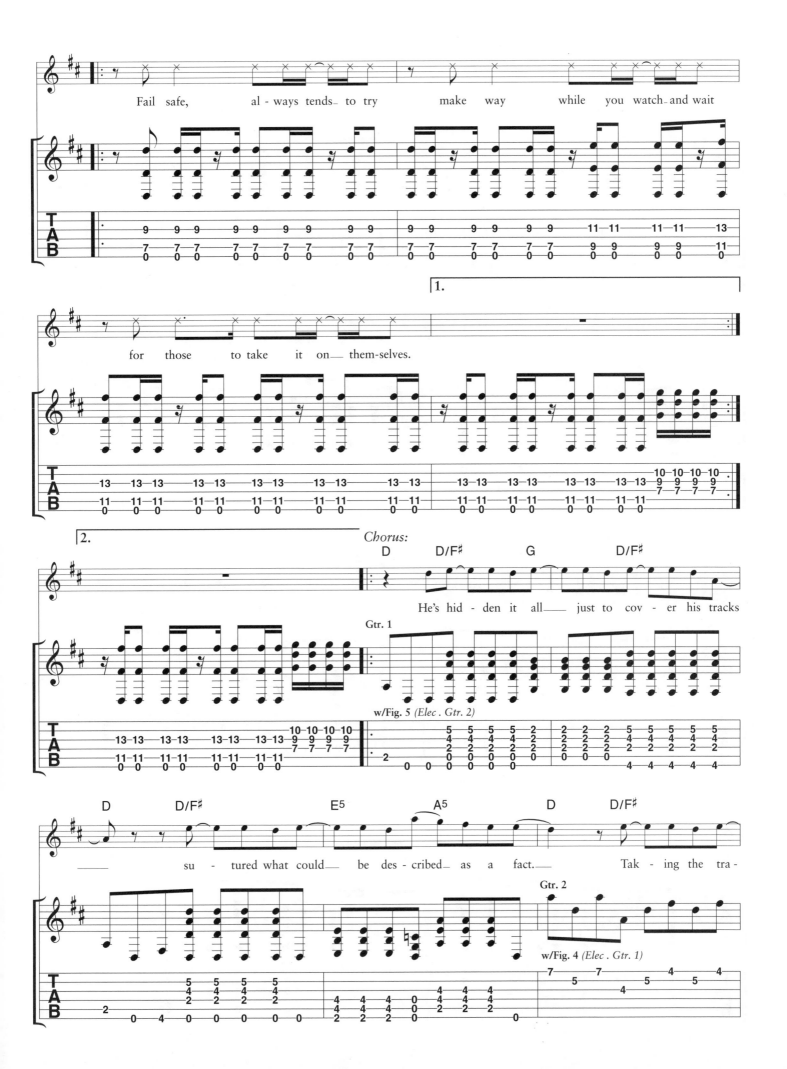

Answers

Words and Music by Andy Bews, Colin Doran, Andy Gilmour, Larry Hibbitt and Paul Townsend

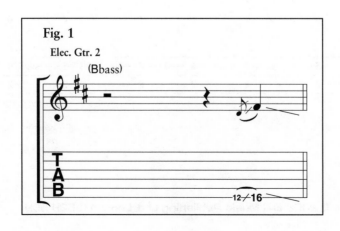

Fig. 1

Elec. Gtr. 2

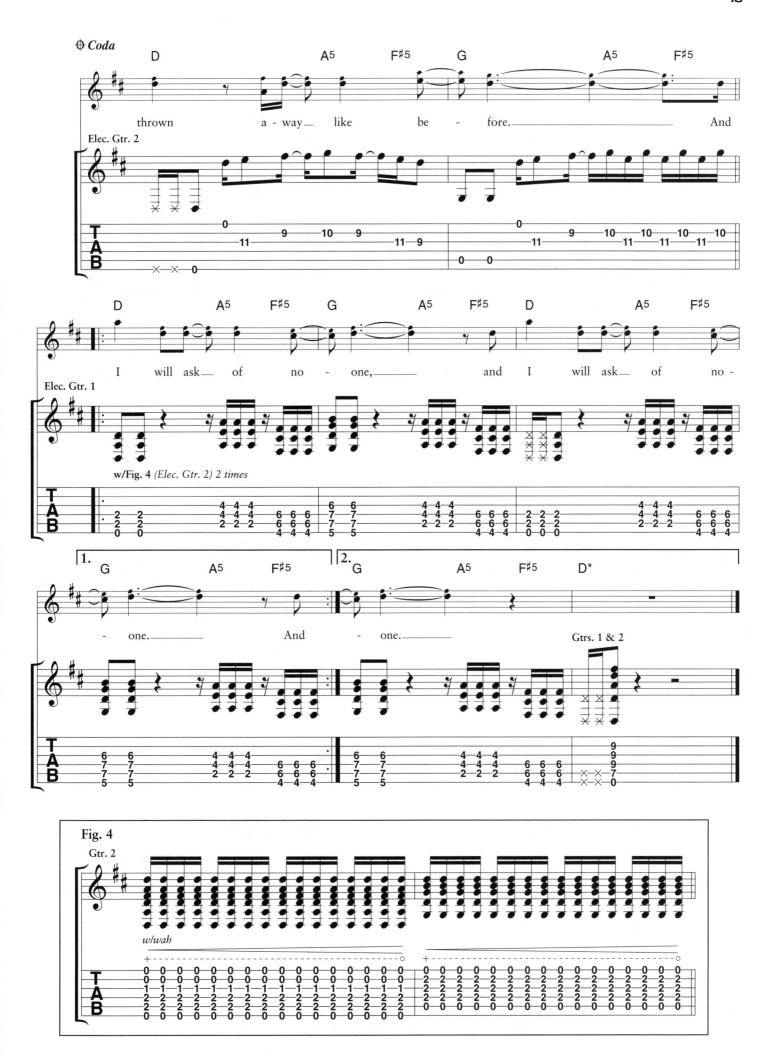

Dissolve

Words and Music by Andy Bews, Colin Doran, Andy Gilmour, Larry Hibbitt and Paul Townsend

Tune all Gtrs.
down 1 tone

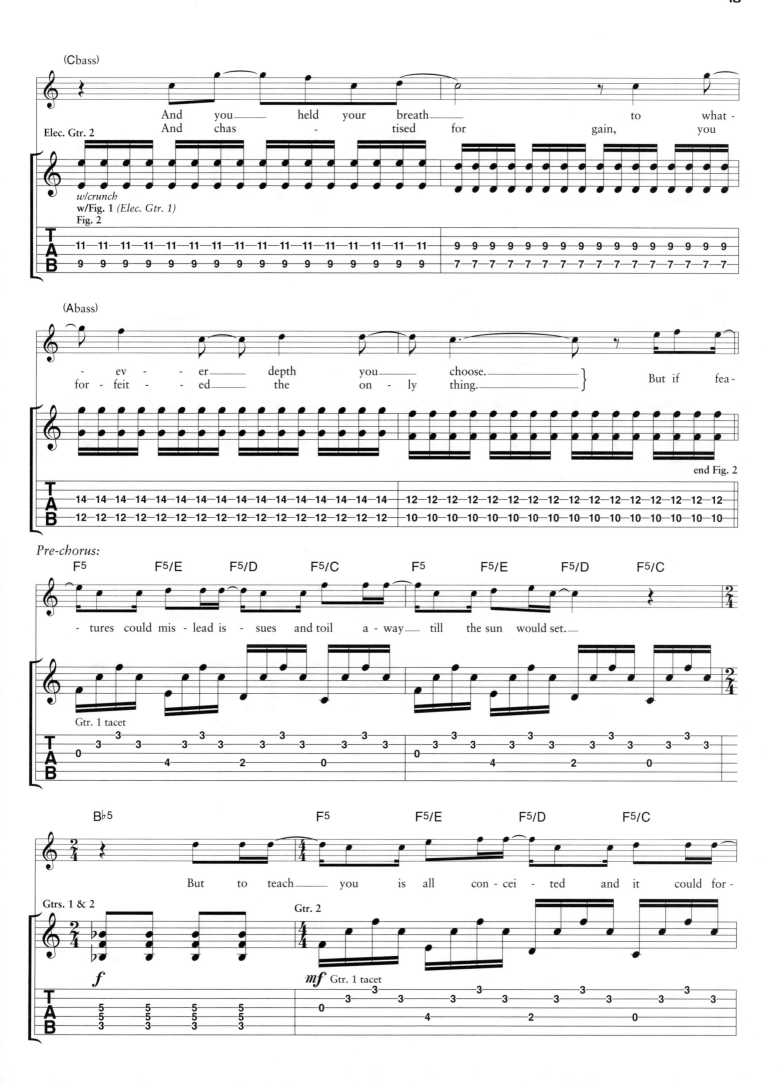

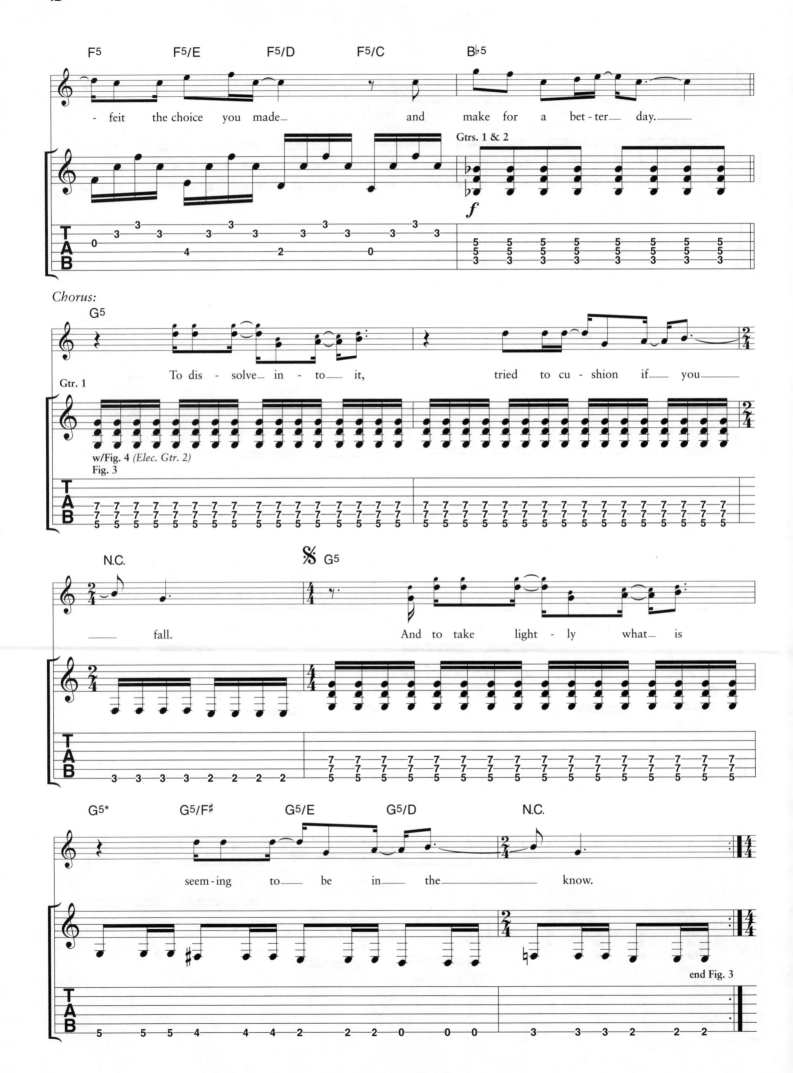

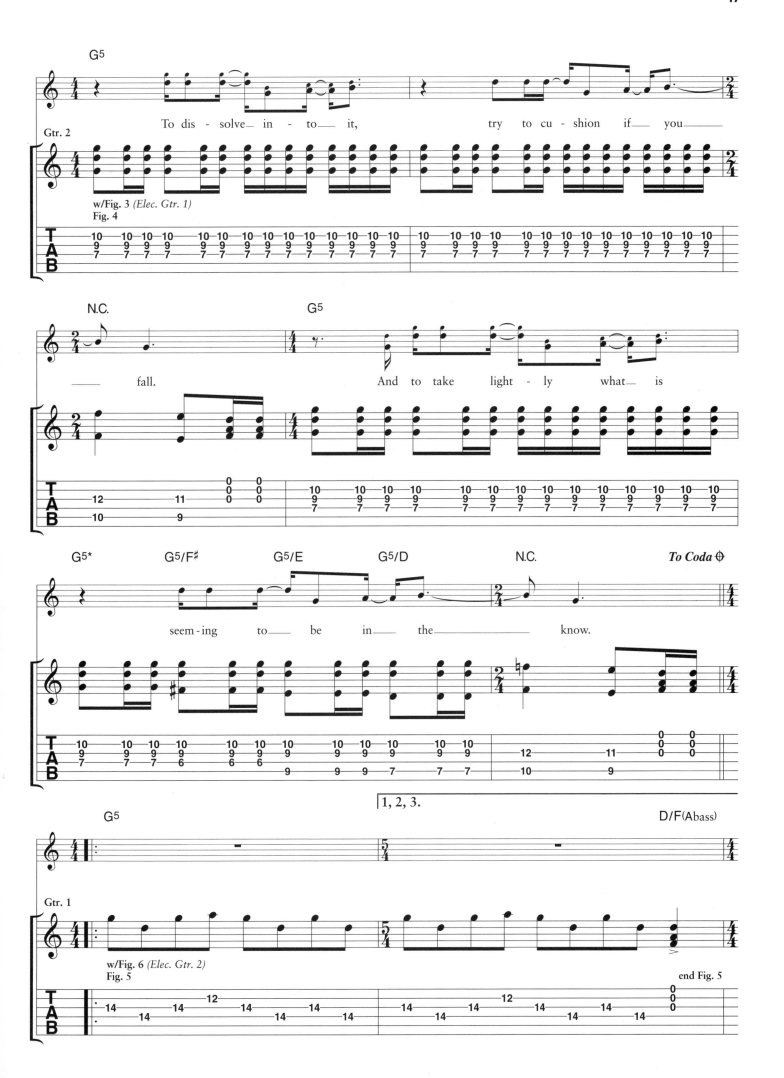

18

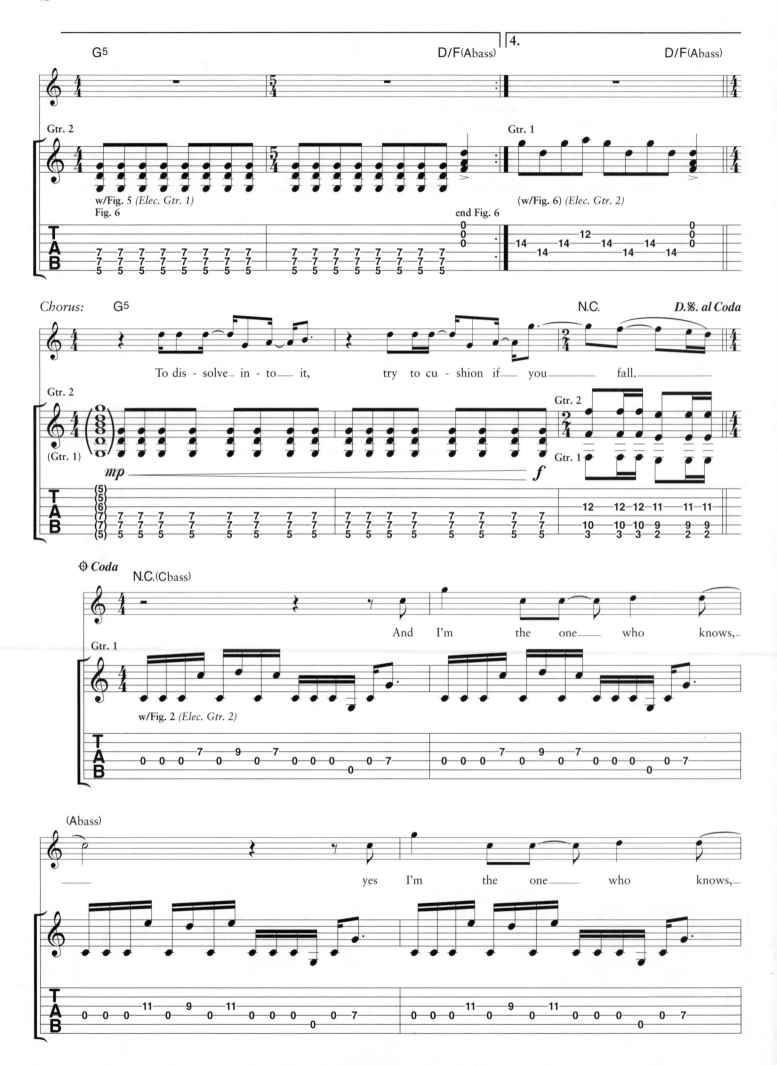

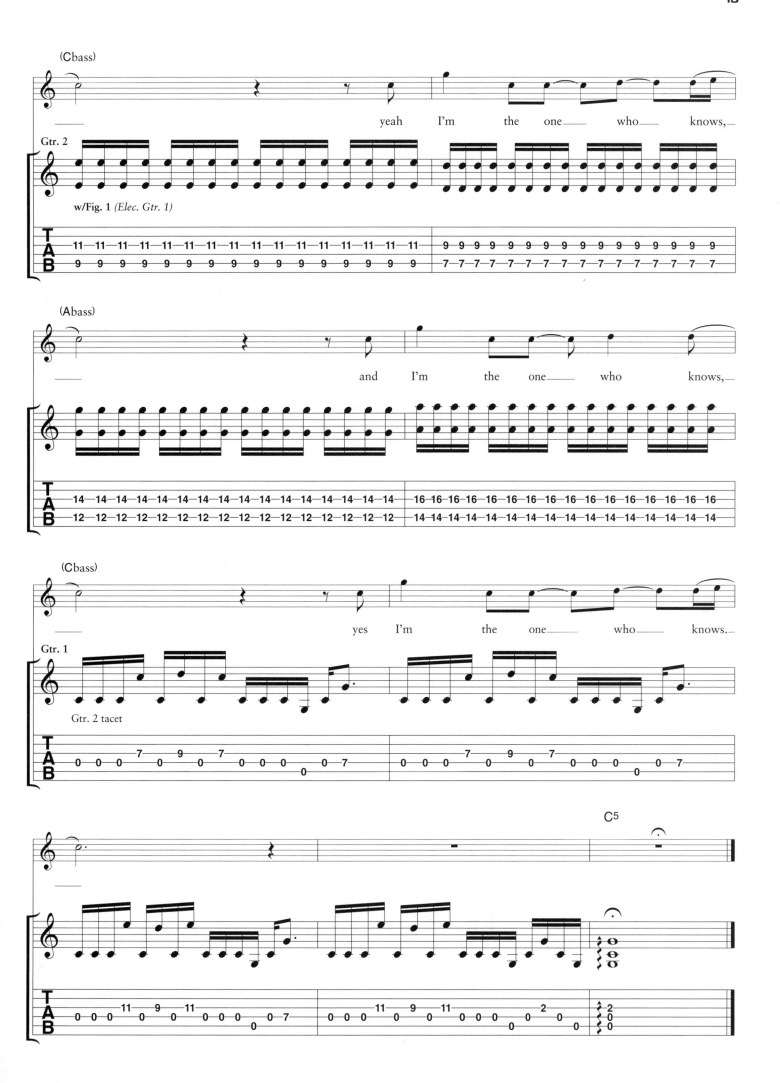

What Thought Did

Words and Music by Andy Bews, Colin Doran, Andy Gilmour, Larry Hibbitt and Paul Townsend

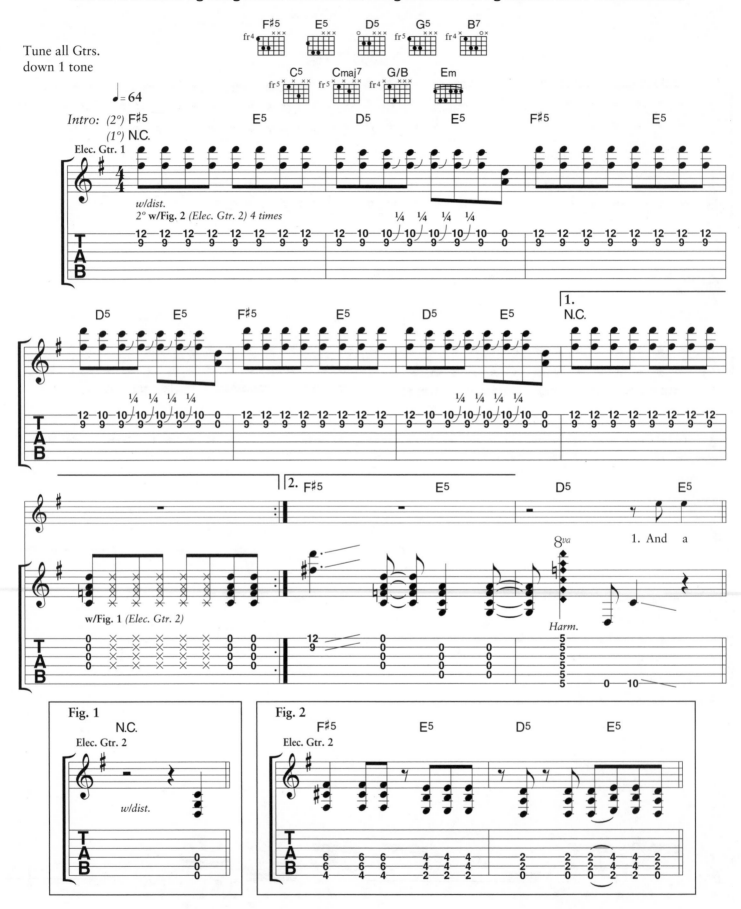

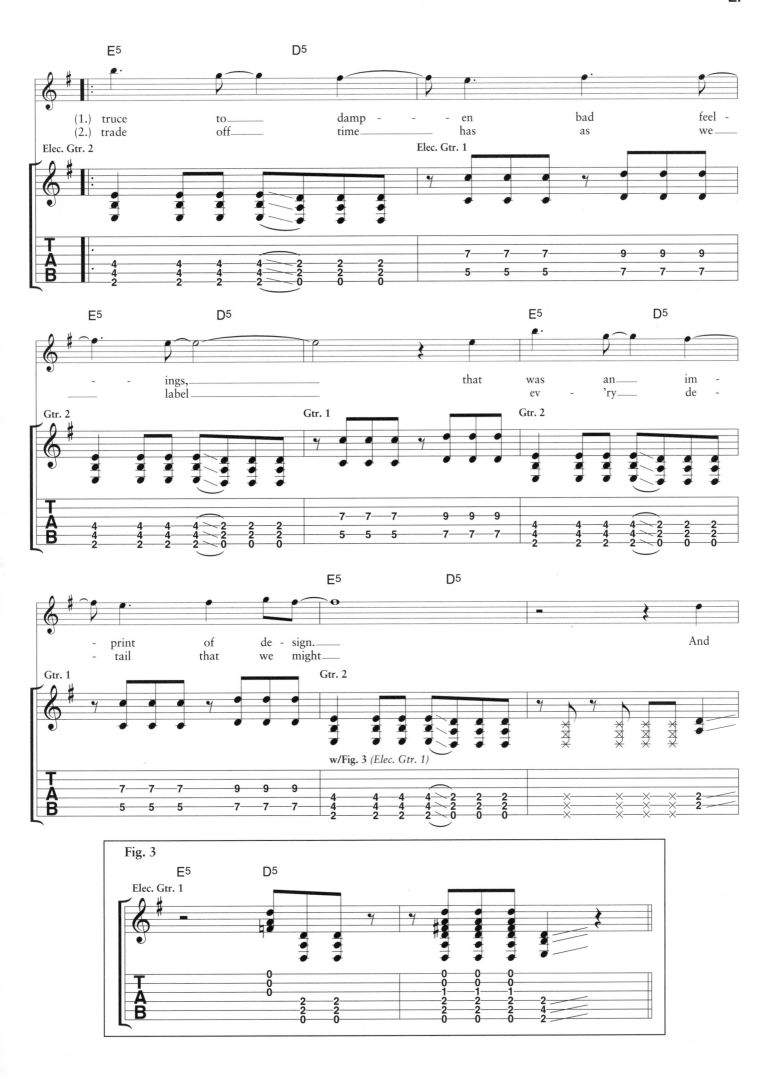

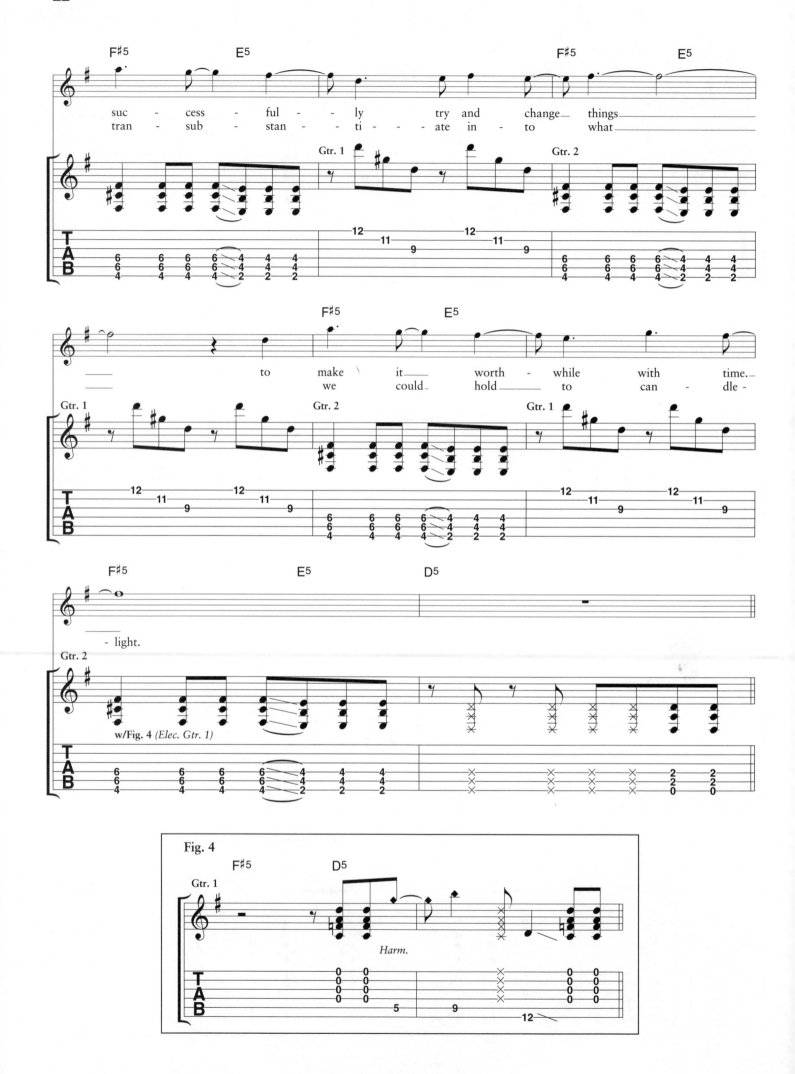

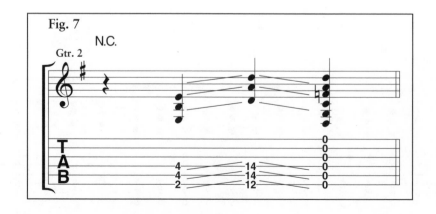

Fig. 7

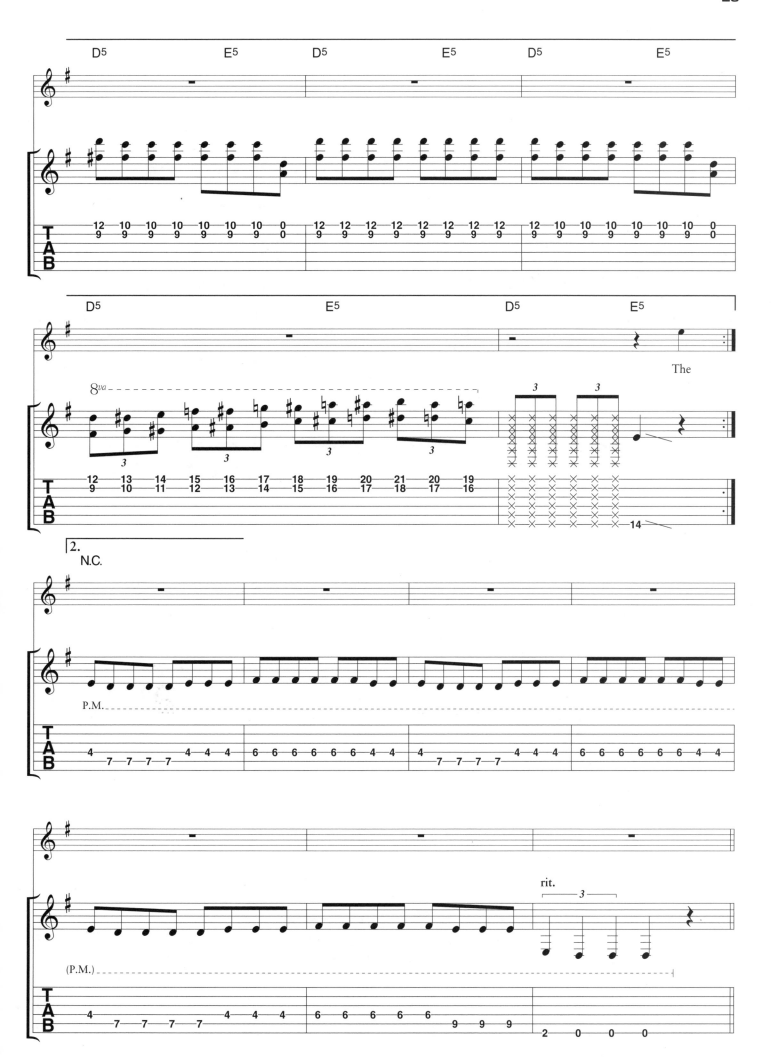

26

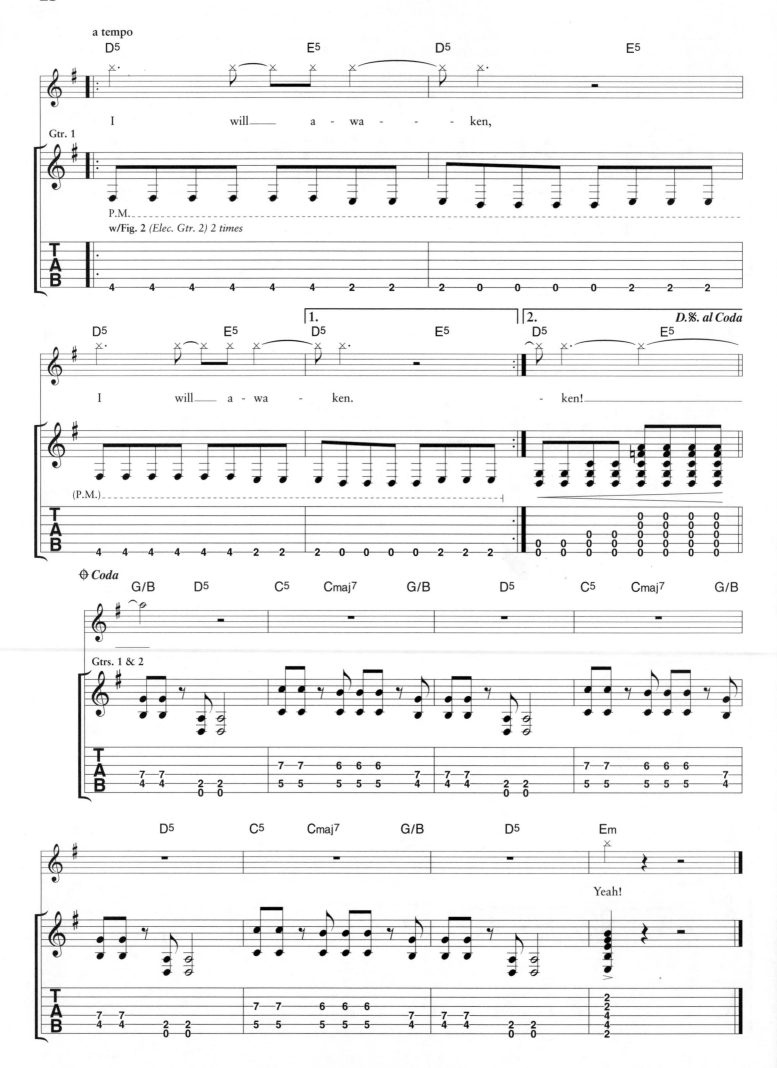

oratorio

Words and Music by Andy Bews, Colin Doran, Andy Gilmour, Larry Hibbitt and Paul Townsend

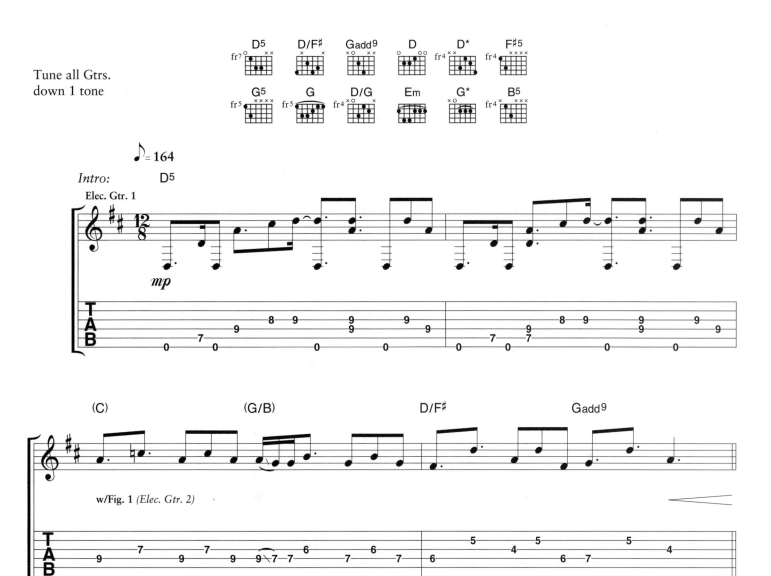

Tune all Gtrs.
down 1 tone

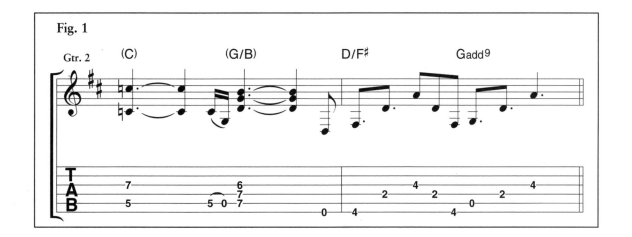

28

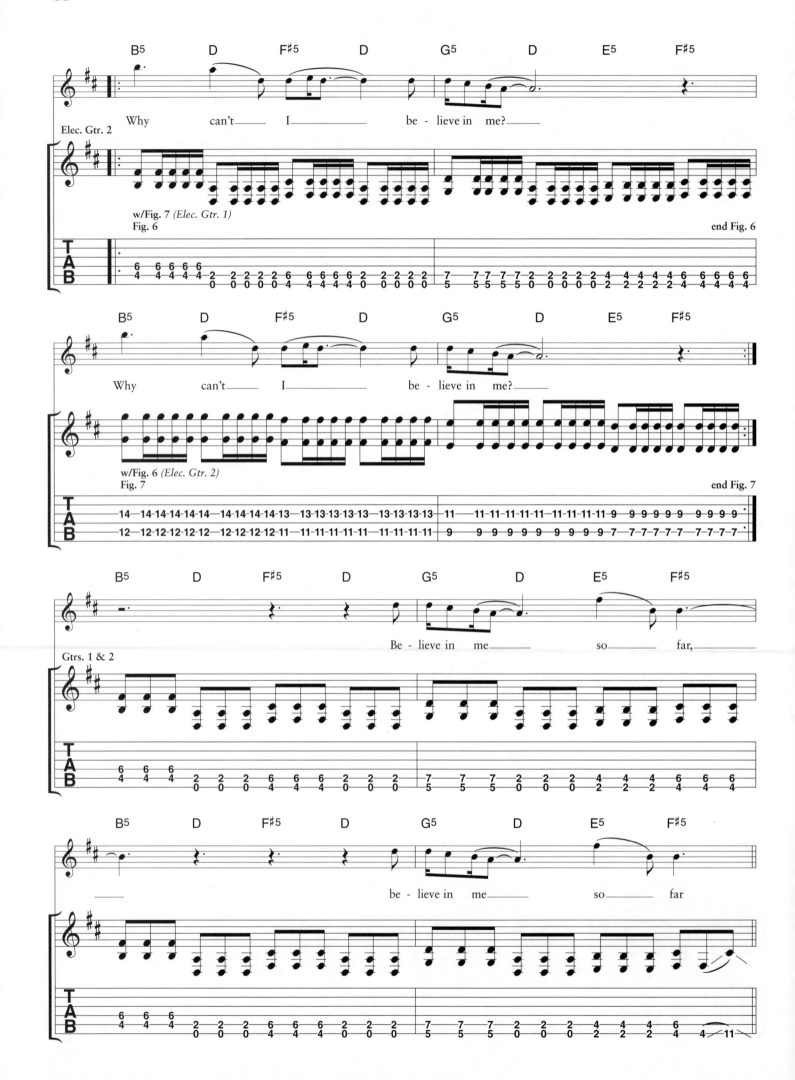

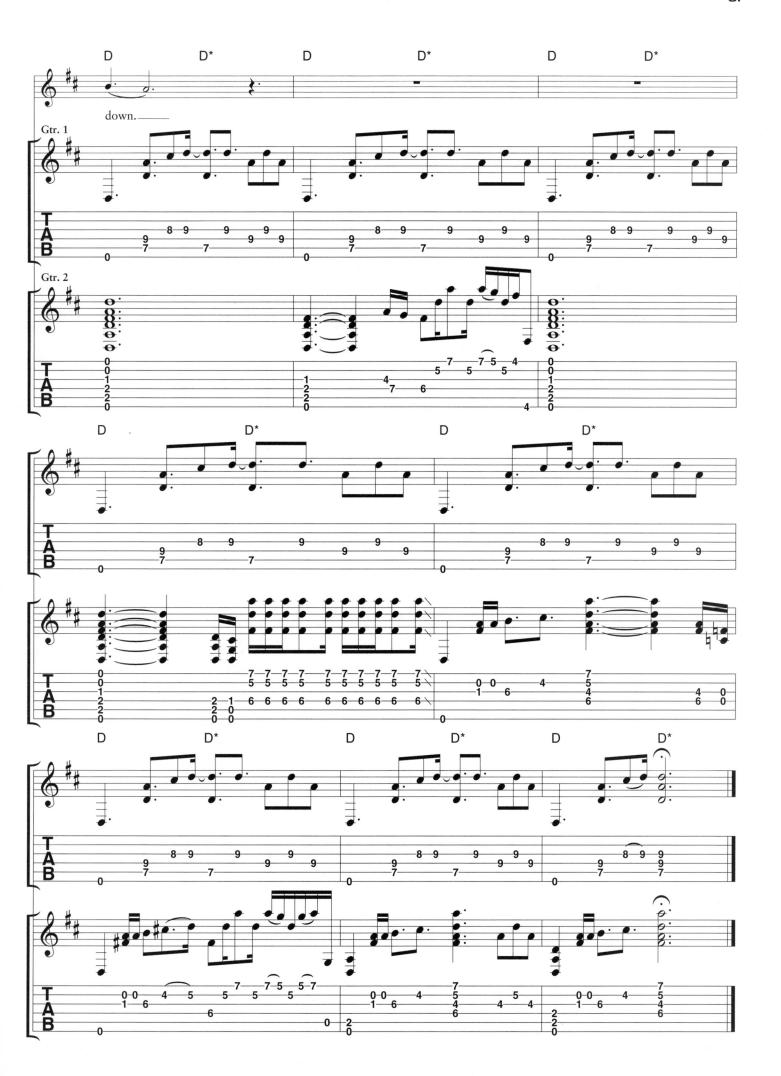

If I could

Words and Music by Andy Bews, Colin Doran, Andy Gilmour, Larry Hibbitt and Paul Townsend

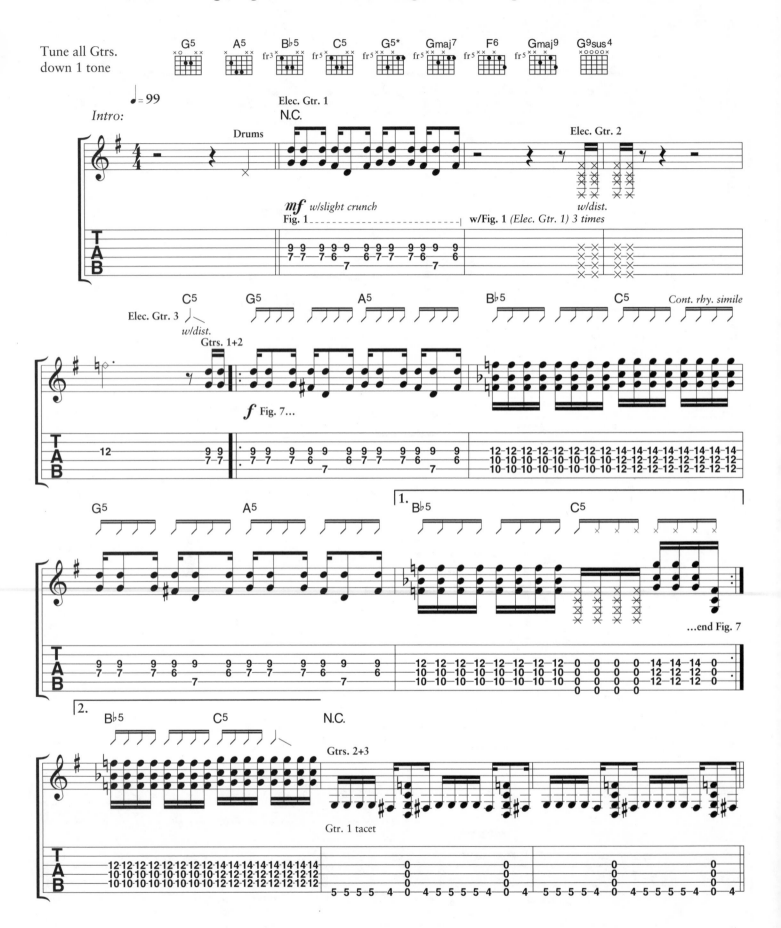

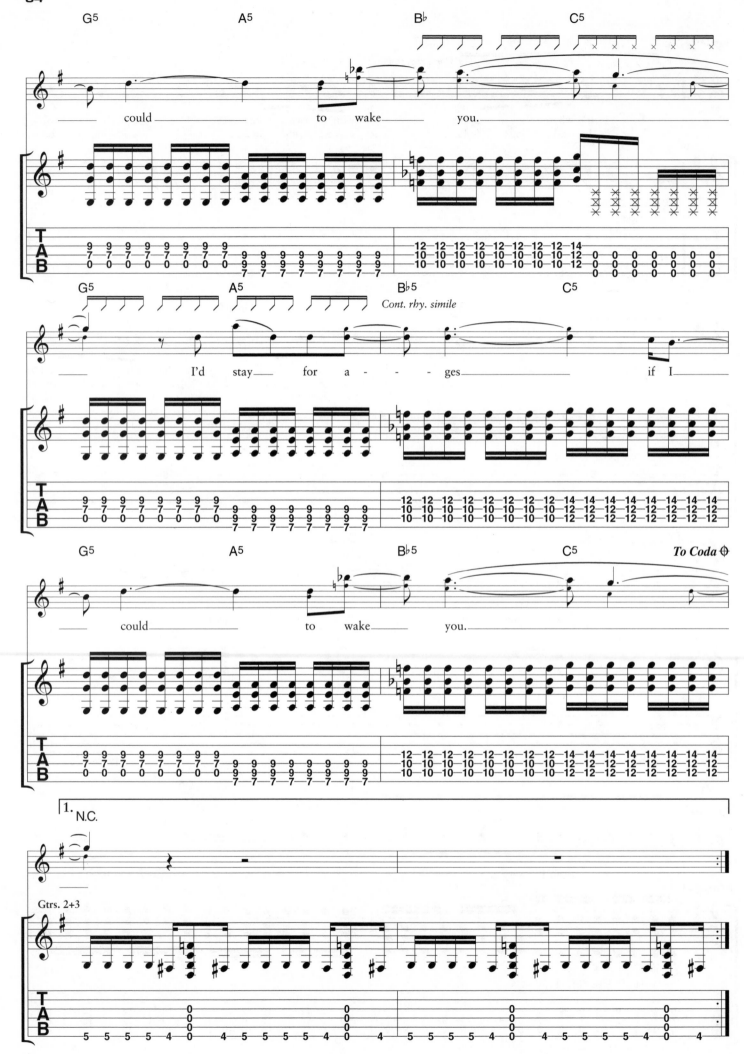

2. *Bridge:*

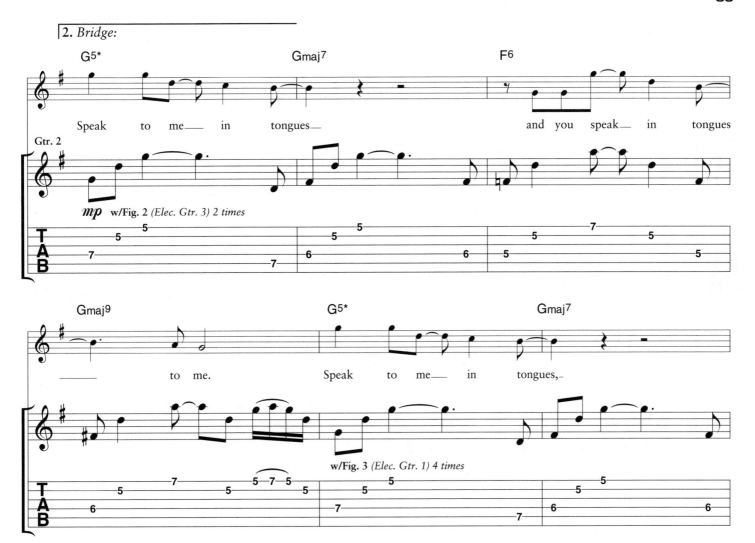

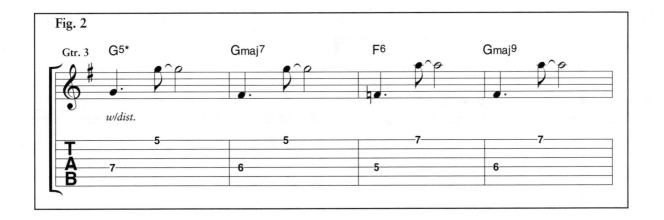

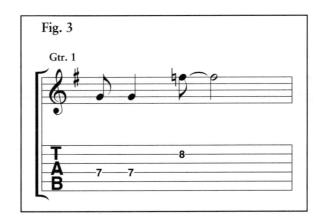

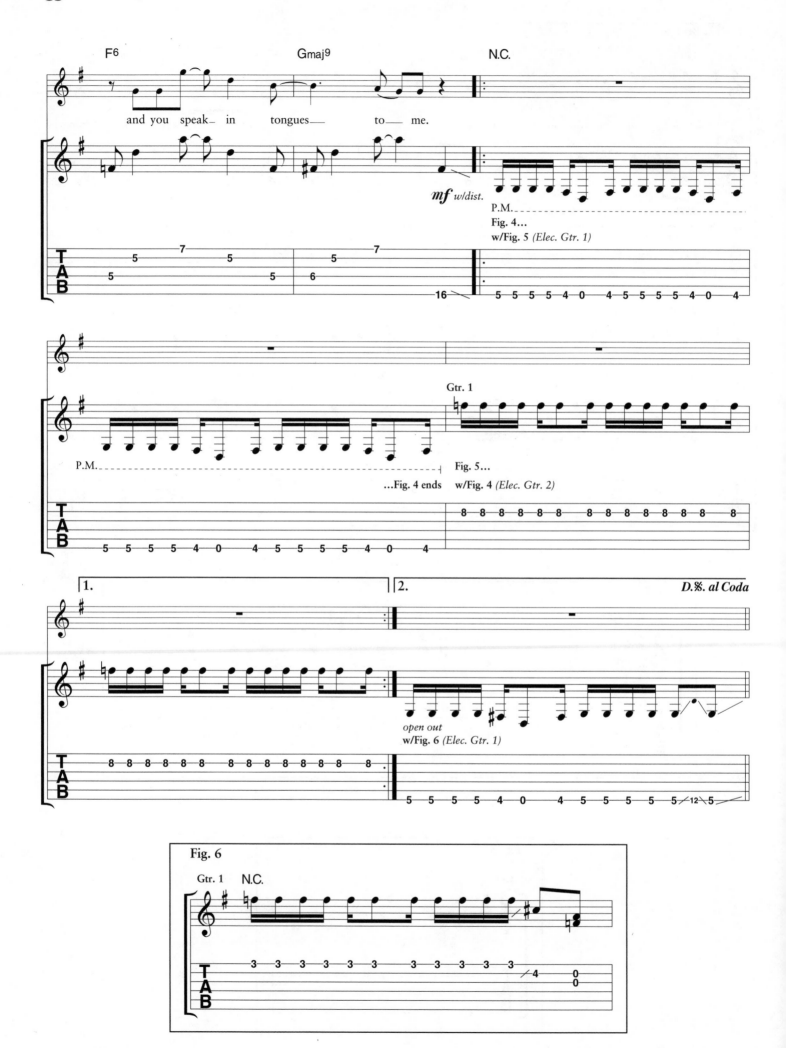

and you speak__ in tongues____ to__ me.

Falter

Words and Music by Andy Bews, Colin Doran, Andy Gilmour, Larry Hibbitt and Paul Townsend

40

shine

Words and Music by Andy Bews, Colin Doran, Andy Gilmour, Larry Hibbitt and Paul Townsend

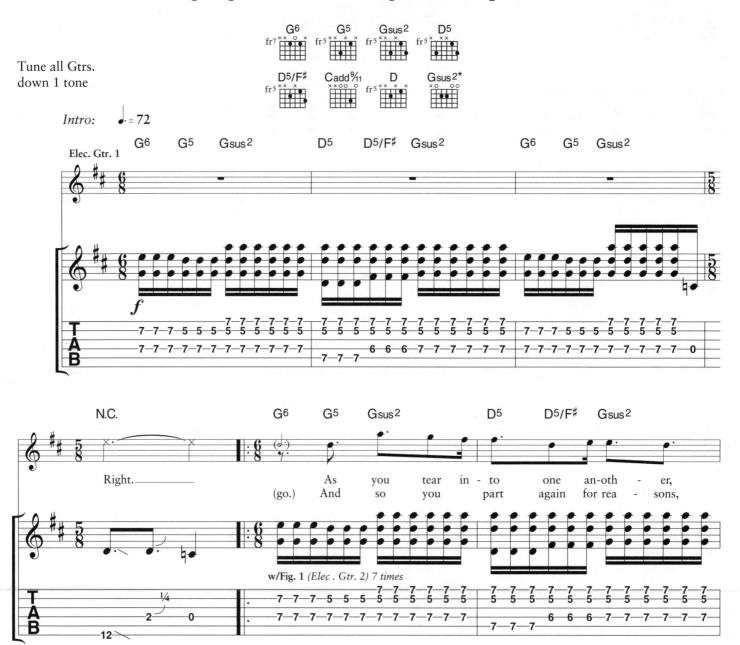

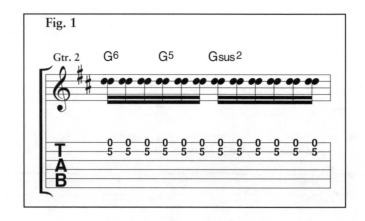

Fig. 1

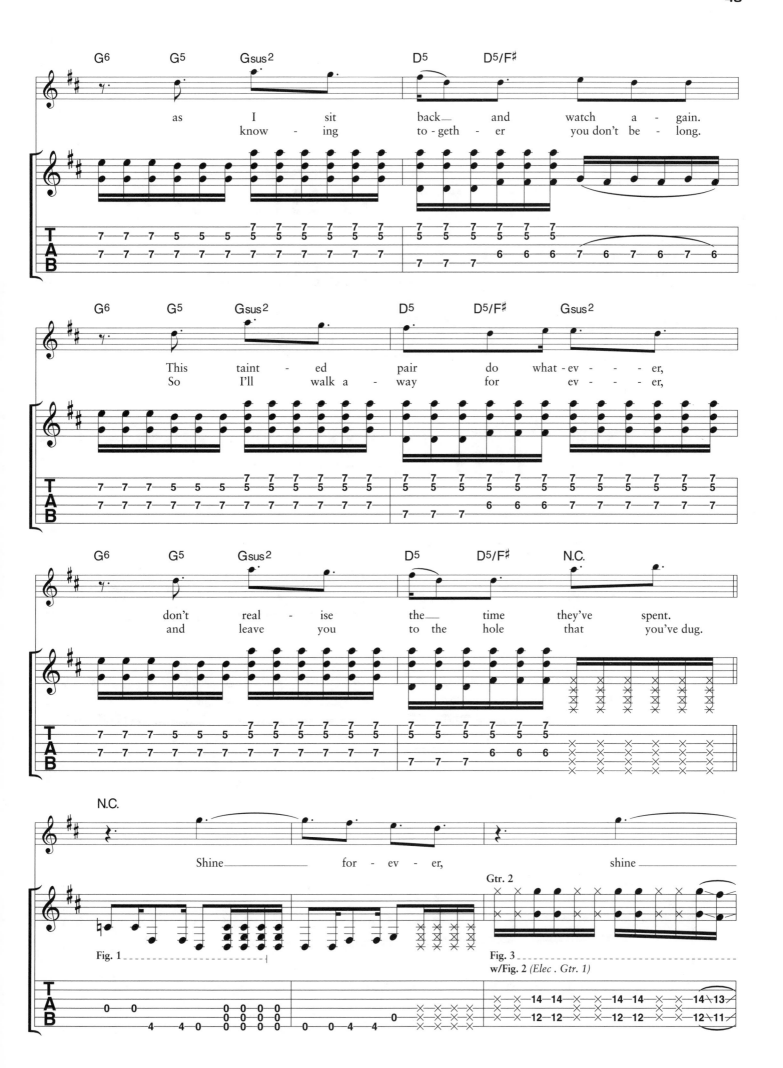

for - ev - er (Let it) shine _____ for - ev - er,

shine _____ for - ev - er _____ don't you (let)

(go.) 3. And so you wait for me to go now, _____

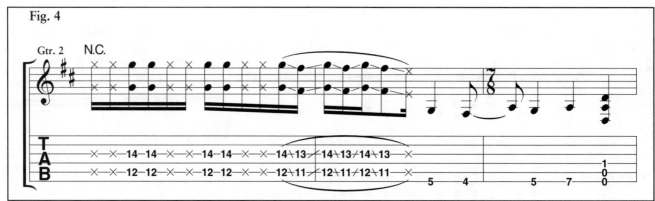

Fig. 4

so you wait for me to go now,

so you wait for me to go now,

so you wait for me to go now.

w/Fig. 5 (Elec . Gtr. 2)

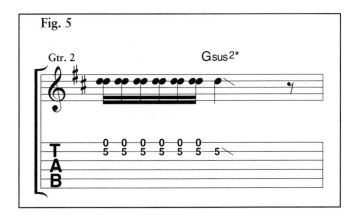

Fig. 5

Drowning

Words and Music by Andy Bews, Colin Doran, Andy Gilmour, Larry Hibbitt and Paul Townsend

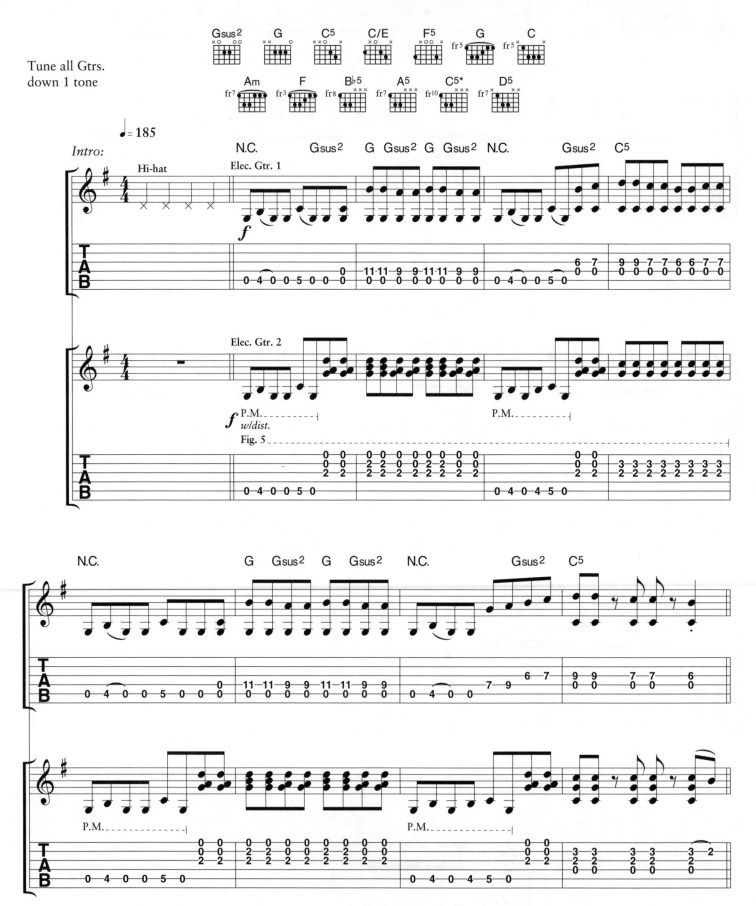

Tune all Gtrs.
down 1 tone

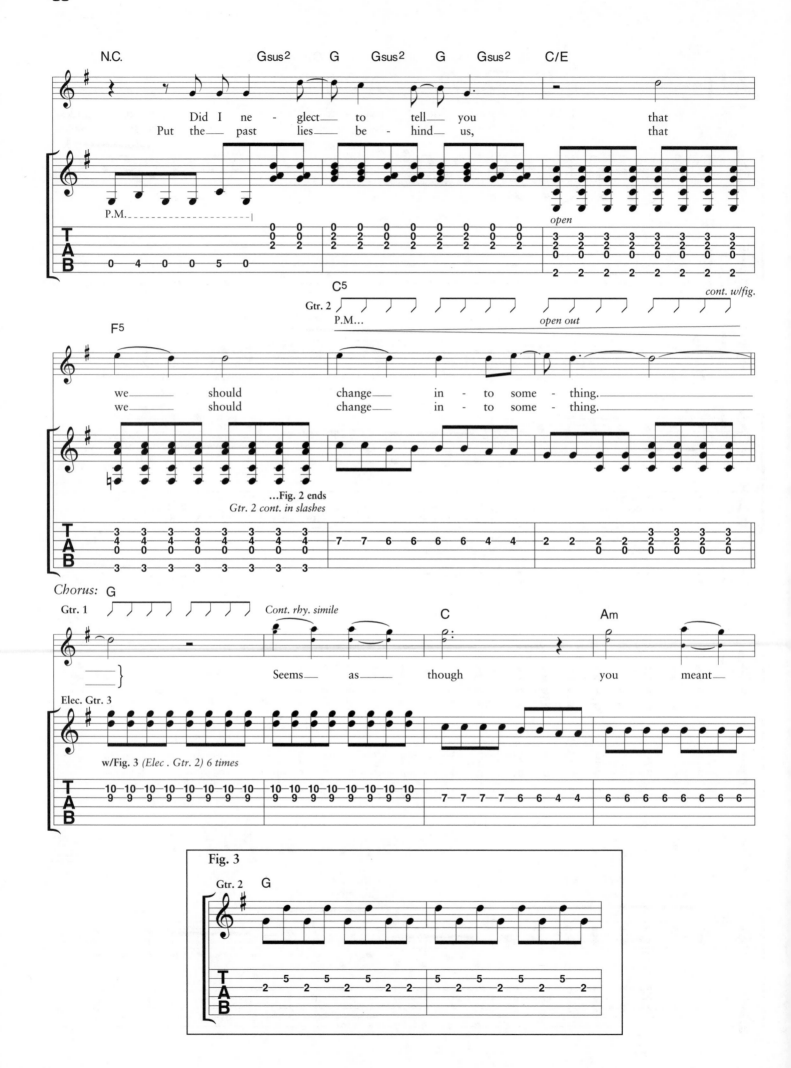

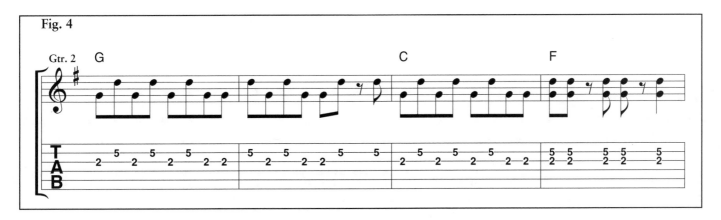

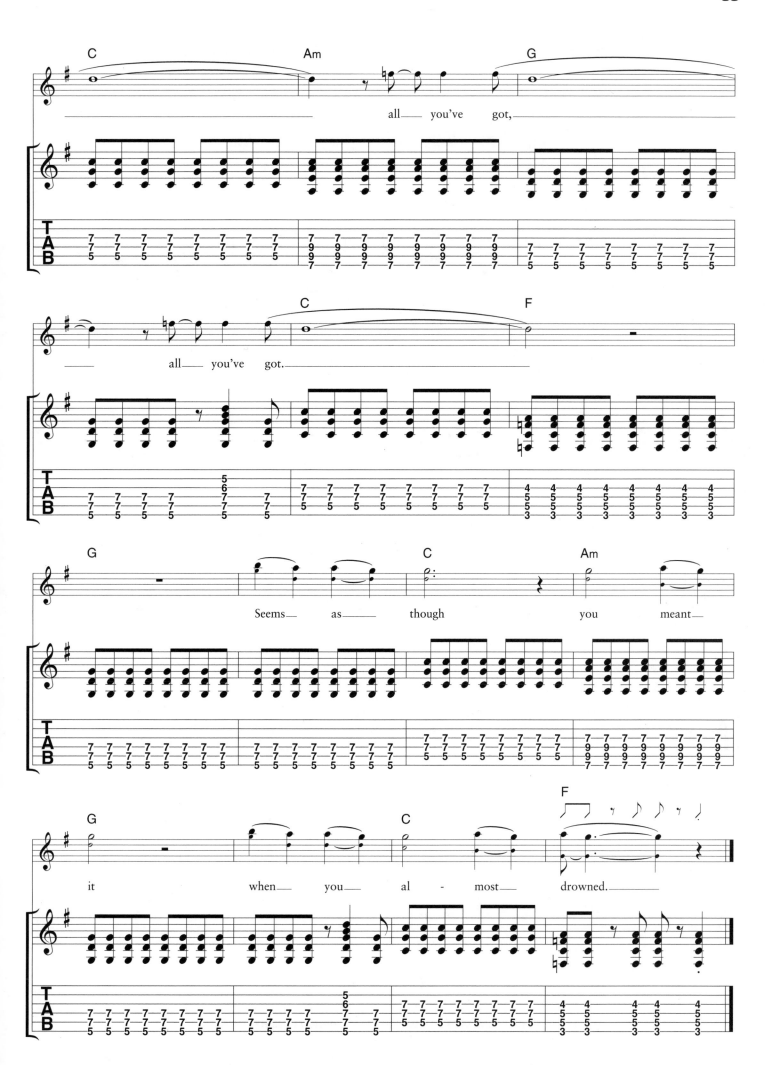

silver

Words and Music by Andy Bews, Colin Doran, Andy Gilmour, Larry Hibbitt and Paul Townsend

Instrumental:

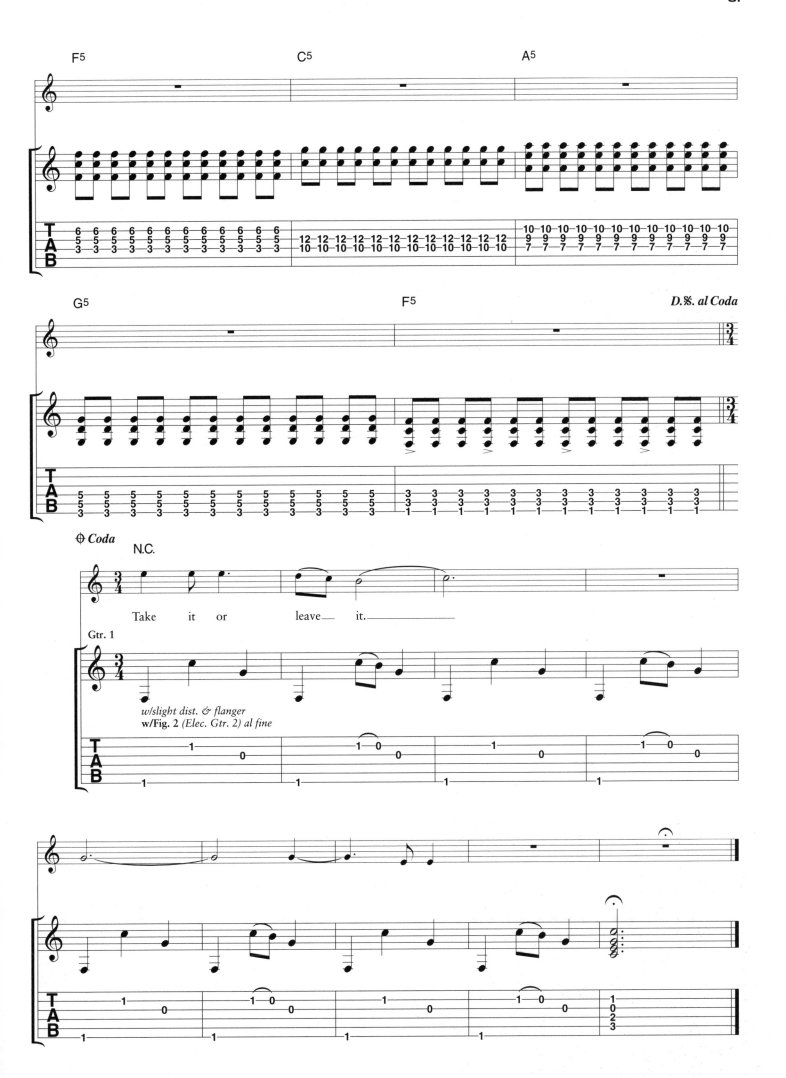

Gone Too Far

Words and Music by Andy Bews, Colin Doran, Andy Gilmour, Larry Hibbitt and Paul Townsend

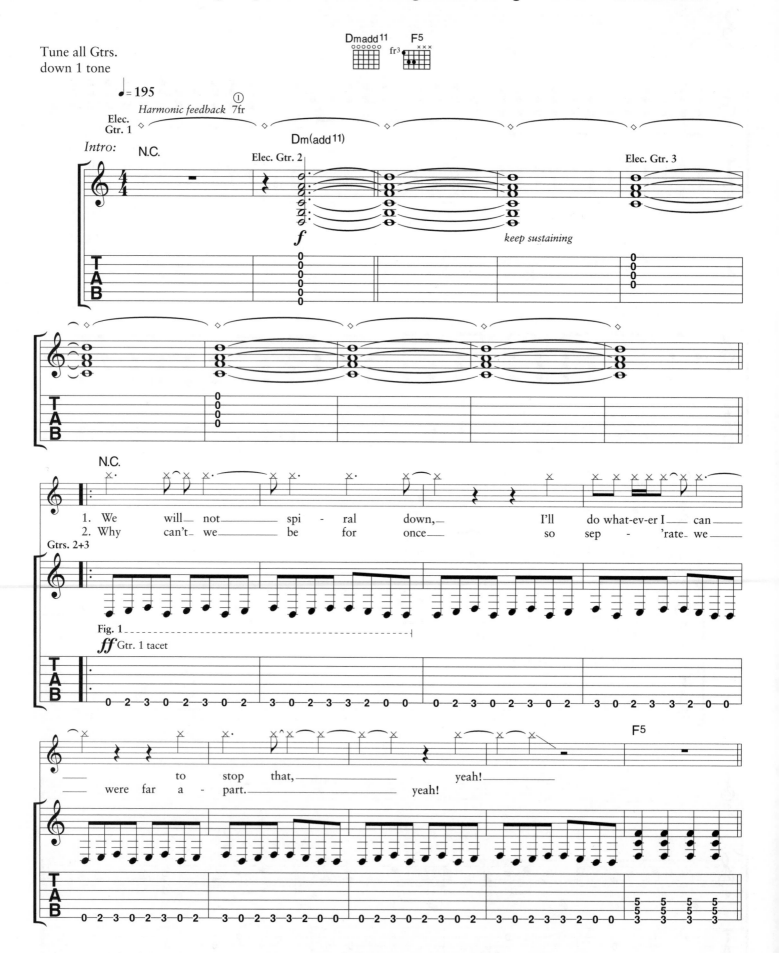

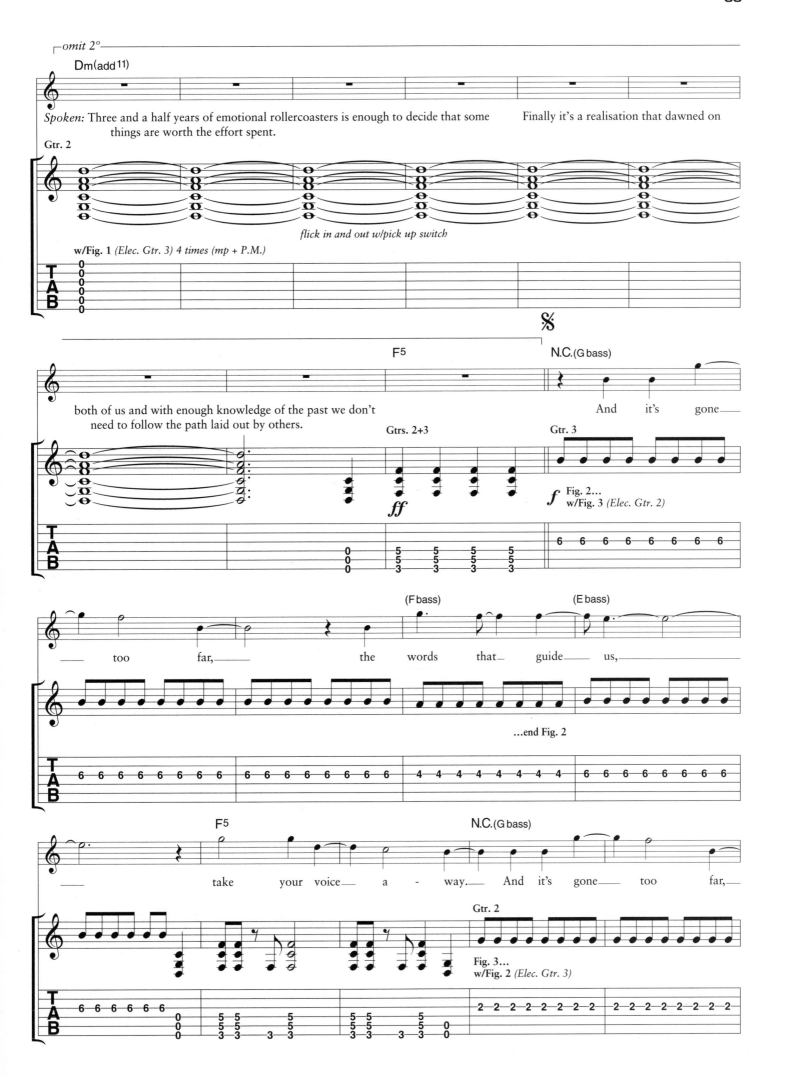

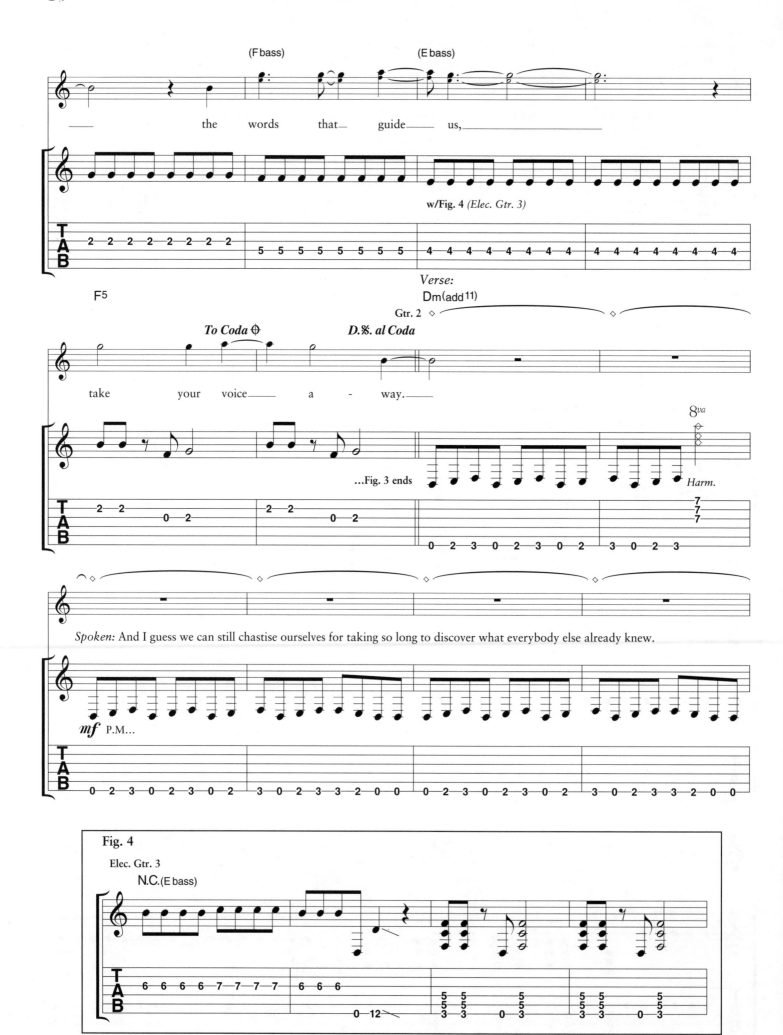

Spoken: And I guess we can still chastise ourselves for taking so long to discover what everybody else already knew.

And all that was needed was an opening of the blinkered eyes long enough to register what was in front of us all along.

Avalanche

Words and Music by Andy Bews, Colin Doran, Andy Gilmour, Larry Hibbitt and Paul Townsend

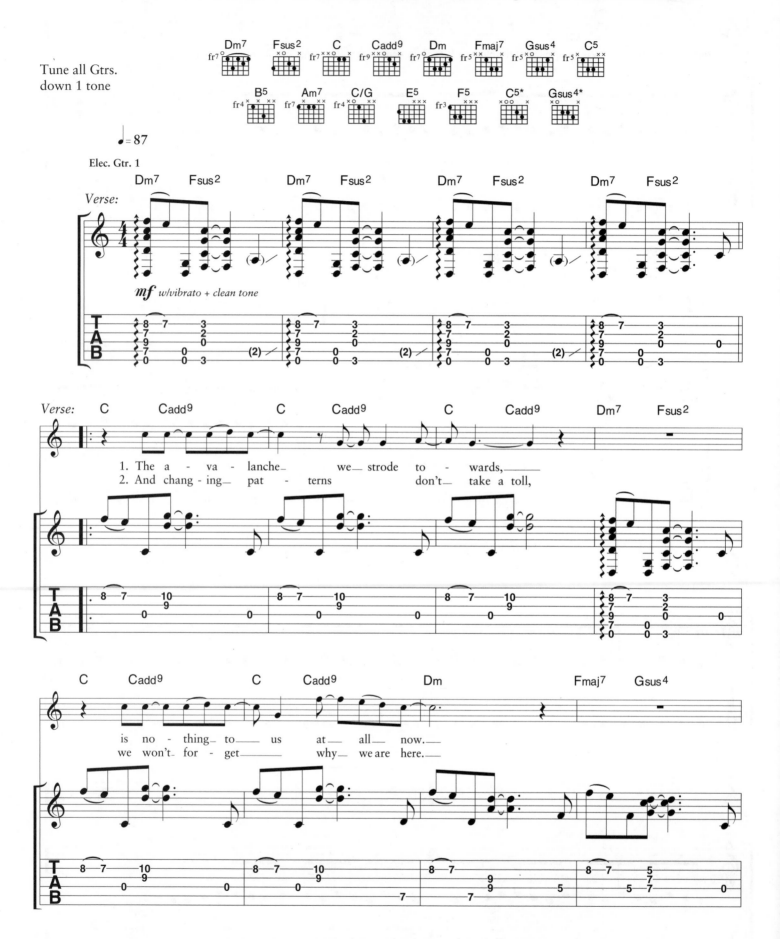

1. The a - va - lanche we strode to - wards,
2. And chang - ing pat - terns don't take a toll,

is no - thing to us at all now.
we won't for - get why we are here.

68

Printed by Halstan & Co. Ltd., Amersham, Bucks., England

Bibliography

Abbreviations:

NS/CHP National Society/Church House Publishing

SU   Scripture Union

CPAS   Church Pastoral Aid Society

REP   Religious Education Press

NCEC   National Christian Education Council

MDEY Methodist Church Division of Education and Youth

JBCE   Joint Board of Christian Education

ICC   International Christian Communications

CHAPTER 1

General books on outreach to children:

All God's Children?, NS/CHP, 1991

P. Butler, *Reaching Children*, SU, 1993

P. Frank, *Children and Evangelism*, CPAS, 1992

J. Hattan, *Family Evangelism*, SU

S. Hutchinson, *Help, I want to tell Kids about Jesus*, SU Missions

M. Breen, *Outside In*, SU, 1991

Books on theories of faith development:

J. Fowler, *Stages of Faith*, Crossroad, 1992

J. Westerhoff, *Will our Children Have Faith?*, Seabury Press, 1976

C. Dykstra, *Faith Development*, REP, 1986

How Faith Grows, NS/CHP, 1991

M. Donaldson, *Children's Minds*, Fontana, 1978

F. Bridger, *Children Finding Faith*, SU, 1986

J. Astley and L. Francis, *Christian Perspectives on Faith Development*, Gracewing, 1994

Other books mentioned in this section:

P. Cliff, *The Rise and Role of the Sunday School Movement in England 1780-1980*, NCEC, 1986

CHAPTER 2

R. Buckland, *Children and God*, SU, 1988

M. Durran, *Understanding Children*, Marshall Pickering, 1987

D. Porter, *Children at Risk*, Kingsway, 1986

N. Postman, *The Disappearance of Childhood*, Laurel Books, 1982

J. Inchley, *Realities of Childhood*, SU, 1985

CHAPTER 3

The Children Act – Guidance for Churches (leaflet), MDEY

Safe From Harm, Home Office, 1994

Good Practice Pack, Lichfield Diocese

Better Safe than Sorry, Oxford Diocese

CHAPTER 4

A. Baumohl, *Grow Your Own Leaders*, SU, 1987

Working with Children (DIY training pack), SU

Team Talk, (DIY training pack), CPAS

Together with Children (resource magazine), NS

Children's Ministry (bi-monthly resource magazine), Elm House Publishing

Leading Children in Churches, CPAS

Organisations which offer training courses:

Church Pastoral Aid
  Society
Athena Drive
Tachbrook Park
Warwick CV34 6NG
Tel: 01926 334242

Scripture Union
207 Queensway
Bletchley
Milton Keynes
MK2 2EB
Tel: 01908 856000

Youth for Christ
Cleobury Place
Cleobury Mortimer
Kidderminster
Worcs DY14 8JG
Tel: 01299 270260

WAY (Waverley Abbey Youth)
Waverley Abbey House
Waverley Lane
Farnham
Surrey GU9 8EP
Tel: 01252 783695

Youth With A Mission
Highfield Oval
Ambrose Lane
Harpenden
Herts AL5 4BX
Tel: 01582 765481

Children Worldwide
Dalesdown
Honeybridge Lane
Dial Post
Horsham
W. Sussex RH13 8NZ
Tel: 04037 101712

Crusaders
2 Romeland Hill
St Albans
Herts AL3 4ET
Tel: 01727 855422

TnT
29 Buxton Gardens
London W3 9LE
Tel: 0181 992 0450

Claire Gibb
Paravel
25 Norreys Avenue
Oxford OX1 4ST
Tel: 01865 249828

Publicity material:
Christian Publicity Organisation
Garcia Estate
Canterbury Road
Worthing
West Sussex BN13 1BW
Tel: 01903 264556

(CPO have a catalogue of ready printed colour publicity material which they can overprint with specific details, or you can do this yourself with a computer and photocopier. They are for use in a Christian context only. You can ask to be put on their mailing list and they will send you samples of new materials and new catalogues when they come out.)

For DIY publicity, the *Instant Art* series of books have photocopiable sheets for use in publicity and newsletters, etc. The series also has books of photocopiable worksheets. They are published by:

Palm Tree Press
Rattlesden
Bury St Edmunds
Suffolk IP30 0SZ

CHAPTER 5

J. Dobson, *The New Dare to Discipline*, Kingsway, 1993

CHAPTER 6

General resources with a mixture of activities:

S. Kirby, *Bible Stories and Activities with the Under Fives – Books 1-6*, CPAS, 1992

C. Orme and C. Wood, *Splash! – a resource book for under 5's*, SU, 1992

K. Copsey and C. Derry, *Bounce! – exciting resources for use with 5-7s*, SU, 1994

S. Clutterham and D. Trotter, *Springboard – helping 7-11 year olds into the Bible*, SU, 1989

J. Godfrey, *Praise, Play and Paint!*, NS/CHP, 1995

S. Vesey, *Easter Activity Book*, Lion

M. Dooney, *The Green Activity Book*, Lion

A. Ludlow, *Festive Fun*, Lion

S. Box, *The Christmas Holiday Fun Book*, Lion

'Trek' teaching material - a set of 16 books for each of the ages 3-6 and 7-11, CPAS

M. Dean (Ed.), *Pick and Mix*, NS/CHP, 1992

N. Currie, *Festive Allsorts*, NS/CHP, 1994

N. Currie and J. Thomson, *Seasons, Saints and Sticky Tape*, NS/CHP, 1992

'Telling' stories:

M. Shelley, *Telling Stories to Children*, Lion, 1990

P. Frank, *The Lion Story Bible*, Lion

The Palm Tree Bible, Palm Tree Press, 1989:
    The Wonderful Stories of Jesus from the New Testament
    The Stories of God and His people from the Old Testament

D. Hall, *Using the Bible with Children*, Bible Society, 1983

S. Holt, *Puppets in Praise*, Marshall Pickering, 1994

S. Relf, *100 Ideas for Children's Talks*, Kingsway, 1994

Drama:

A. Smith, *Much Ado About Something*, CPAS, 1995

D. Hopwood, *Acting Up*, NS/CHP, 1995

D. Hopwood, *A Fistful of Sketches*, NS/CHP, 1996

D. Haylock, *Plays on the Word*, NS/CHP, 1993

D. Haylock, *Sketches from Scripture*, NS/CHP, 1992

P. Powell, *Scenes and Wonders*, NS/CHP, 1994

Games:

K. Anderson and M. Carlson, *Games for all occasions*, Zondervan, 1967

P. Baker, *Simulation games 1 – 4*, JBCE, 1986

P. Goodland, *Over 300 Games for all occasions* (revised edition), SU, 1995

L. Pinchbeck, *Theme Games*, SU, 1993

Craft:

The Usborne book of Masks, Usborne, 1993

The Usborne book of Face Painting, Usborne, 1993

Snazaroo, *Five Minute Faces*, Kingfisher, 1992

Children's Art and Crafts and *More Children's Art and Crafts*, Australian Women's Weekly

D. Einon, *Creative Play*, Penguin

Inspirations, Bright Ideas, Scholastic

L. Rock, *The Simply Wonderful Craftbook*, Lion

Help! I Can't Draw – books 1-4, CPAS

Singing:

Junior Praise, Marshall Pickering, 1986

Mission Praise, Marshall Pickering, 1983

Songs of Fellowship for Kids, Kingsway, 1992

Kids Praise, ICC/Spring Harvest

M.V. Old (Ed.), *Praise God Together*, SU, 1984

M.V Old and E.M. Stephenson (Ed.), *Sing to God*, SU, 1985

Prayer:

H. Gompertz, *First Prayers*, SU

H. Gompertz, *My Book of Prayers*, SU

J. Harmer, *Prayers for Children*, SU

C. Watson, *365 Children's Prayers*, Lion

M. Batchelor, *The Lion Book of Children's Prayers*, Lion

C. Herbert, *Prayers for Children*, NS/CHP, 1993

Puzzles and worksheets:

Instant Art for Bible Worksheets Books 1-4 Palm Tree Press/ Kevin Mayhew, 1989, 1990, 1994

R. Green, *Over 120 Quizzes for All Occasions*, SU

Bible Puzzletime Books 1 and 2, SU, 1993

Bible Story Puzzle Books 1-4, Candle Books